Diana Kimpton

OXFORD
UNIVERSITY PRESS

Great Clarendon Street, Oxford OX2 6DP

Oxford University Press is a department of the University of Oxford.
It furthers the University's objective of excellence in research, scholarship, and education by publishing worldwide in

Oxford New York

Athens Auckland Bangkok Bogotá Buenos Aires Calcutta
Cape Town Chennai Dar es Salaam Delhi Florence Hong Kong Istanbul
Karachi Kuala Lumpur Madrid Melbourne Mexico City Mumbai
Nairobi Paris São Paulo Singapore Taipei Tokyo Toronto Warsaw

with associated companies in Berlin Ibadan

Oxford is a registered trade mark of Oxford University Press
in the UK and in certain other countries

Published in the United Kingdom
by Oxford University Press

First published 2000

British Library Cataloguing in Publication Data

Data available

ISBN 0 19 915707 3

Available in packs

Weather Pack of Six	(one of each book)	ISBN 0 19 915711 1
Weather Class Pack	(six of each book)	ISBN 0 19 915712 X

Printed in Hong Kong

Acknowledgements

The Publisher would like to thank the following for permission to reproduce photographs:

Corbis: front cover; Corel: title page, contents page, p 9 (*top right*); index page; Robert Harding Picture Library/Nick Wood: p 4; The Met. Office/J. F. P. Galvin: p 9 (*bottom left*); Frank Lane Picture Library/David Hosking: p11; Robert Harding Picture Library/P. Hattenberger: p 12 and back cover; Science Photo Library/Dr. Jeremy Burgess: p 13 (*left*); Robert Harding Picture Library/Roy Rainford: p 13 (*right*).

Illustrations by Julian Baker, Lisa Berkshire, Andy Cooke, Tony Morris, and Linda Schwab.

Contents

What is a rainbow?

A rainbow is a beautiful arch of colour in the sky. Rainbows only appear in the sky if the sun shines on rain.

A rainbow is made of coloured light. You can see it but you cannot touch it. You can walk towards it but you will never reach it.

Rainbows have always fascinated people.

The colours of the rainbow

Rainbows are made up of seven bands of colour. They are always in this order with the red on the outside.

FACT BOX

Scientists call the colours of the rainbow the spectrum.

Some people use special sayings to help them remember the colours. Each word begins with the same letter as one of the colours.

How a rainbow is made

You see a rainbow when the sun shines and there are raindrops in the air. Each raindrop is a tiny ball of water.

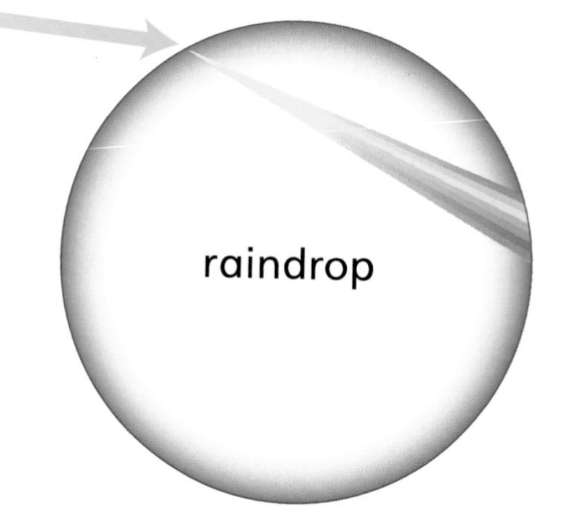

Light from the sun goes into each raindrop. The light splits into different colours.

FACT BOX

The light bends as it goes into the raindrop. We say it is refracted.

The coloured light does not stay inside the raindrop. It hits the back of the raindrop and bounces out.

The light bounces off the back of the raindrop like a ball bounces off a wall.

The coloured light from millions of raindrops makes the rainbow.

FACT BOX

When the coloured light bounces out of the raindrop, we say it is reflected.

Rainbow facts

Some rainbows are higher than other rainbows. In the middle of the day, the sun is high in the sky. It makes a rainbow with a low arch. Sometimes the rainbow arch is so low that you cannot see it easily.

A rainbow in the middle of the day.

Early in the morning and late in the afternoon, the sun is low in the sky. It makes a rainbow with a high arch. You can see the high arch easily.

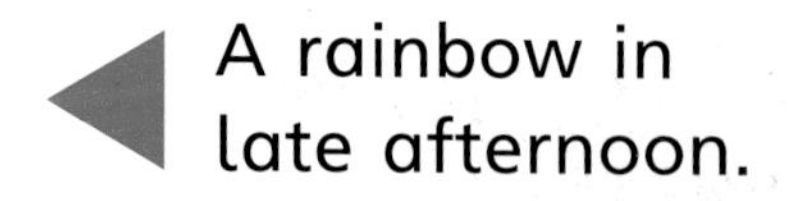

A rainbow in late afternoon.

If you are flying in an aeroplane you can sometimes see circular rainbows on the clouds below.

These rainbows are pale and small. They are called "glories".

If you are very lucky, you may see two rainbows together. The second one is called a secondary bow. A secondary bow is not as bright as an ordinary rainbow. It has the same colours but they are the other way round. The red is on the inside of the arch.

Finding rainbows

The best time to see a rainbow is when the rain is stopping and the sun has started to come out. Stand with your back to the sun and the rain in front of you. Then look in the direction of your shadow. You might see a rainbow in the sky.

Stand between the sun and rain to see a rainbow.

FACT BOX

Look for rainbows early in the morning or late in the afternoon (see page 8 to find out why).

Rainbows without rain

A garden sprinkler sends drops of water into the air. The spray from a fountain or a waterfall is made of drops of water too. These drops are like raindrops, so they can split light. They can make a rainbow when it is not raining.

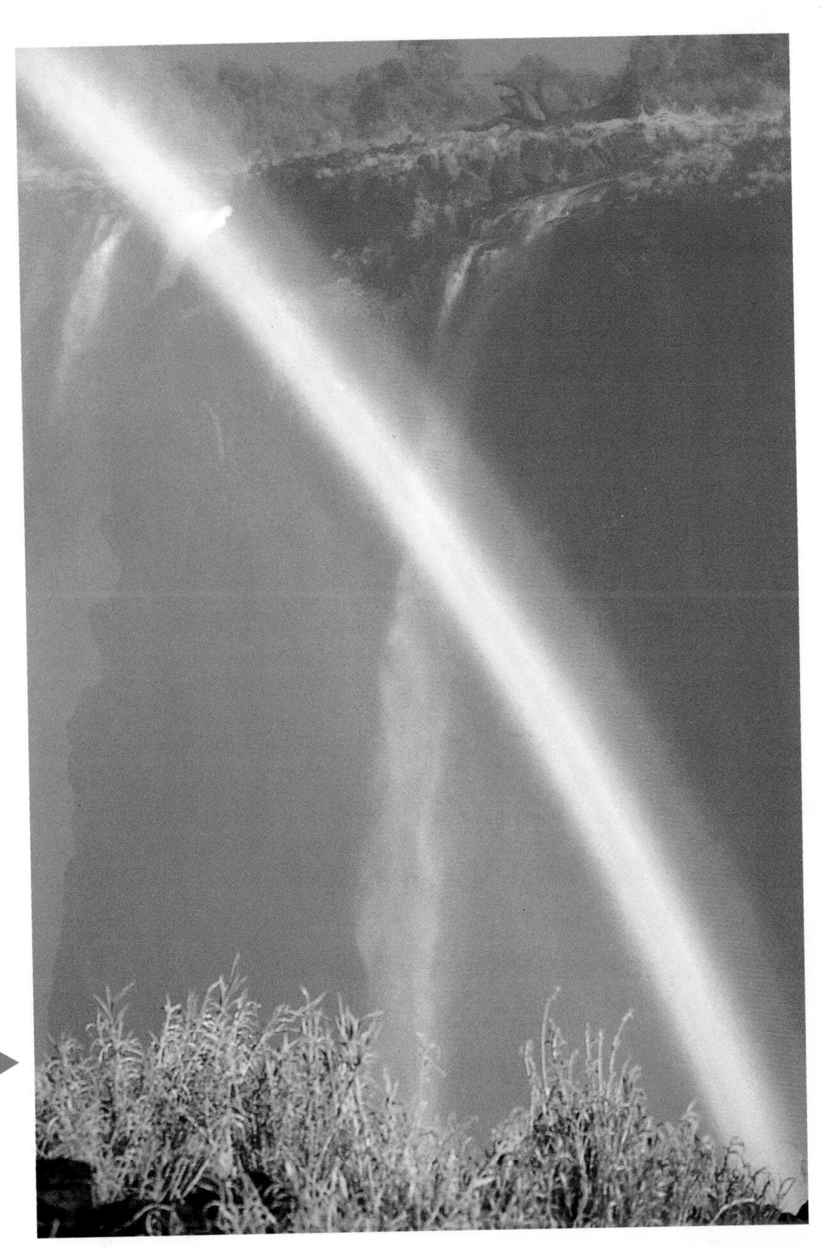

A waterfall can make a rainbow.

Rainbow colours in other places

You see rainbows in the sky. But sometimes you can see the colours of a rainbow in other places too.

Bubbles can split light into the seven bands of colour. You can often see the colours of the rainbow on the outside of bubbles.

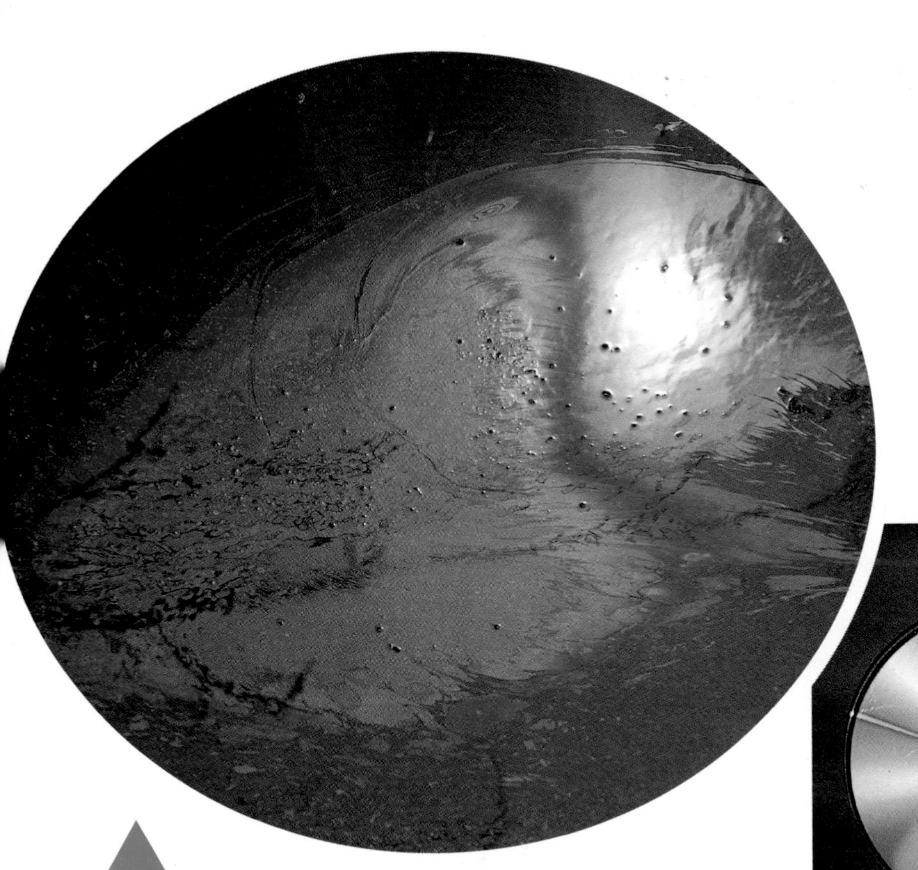

Sometimes you can see
the colours of the rainbow
when you look at a puddle.
This happens when there
is oil on top of the water.

You can often see the colours
of the rainbow when you
look at the silver side of a CD.
If you move the CD gently,
the colours will move too.

Rainbow myths

Long ago, people thought rainbows were magic. People told stories about rainbows. The stories are called myths.

One myth says there is a pot of gold hidden at the end of a rainbow. No one can reach the end of the rainbow, so no one can find the gold.

The arch of the rainbow looks like a bridge. In Greek myths, a goddess called Iris crosses the rainbow bridge to reach the earth.

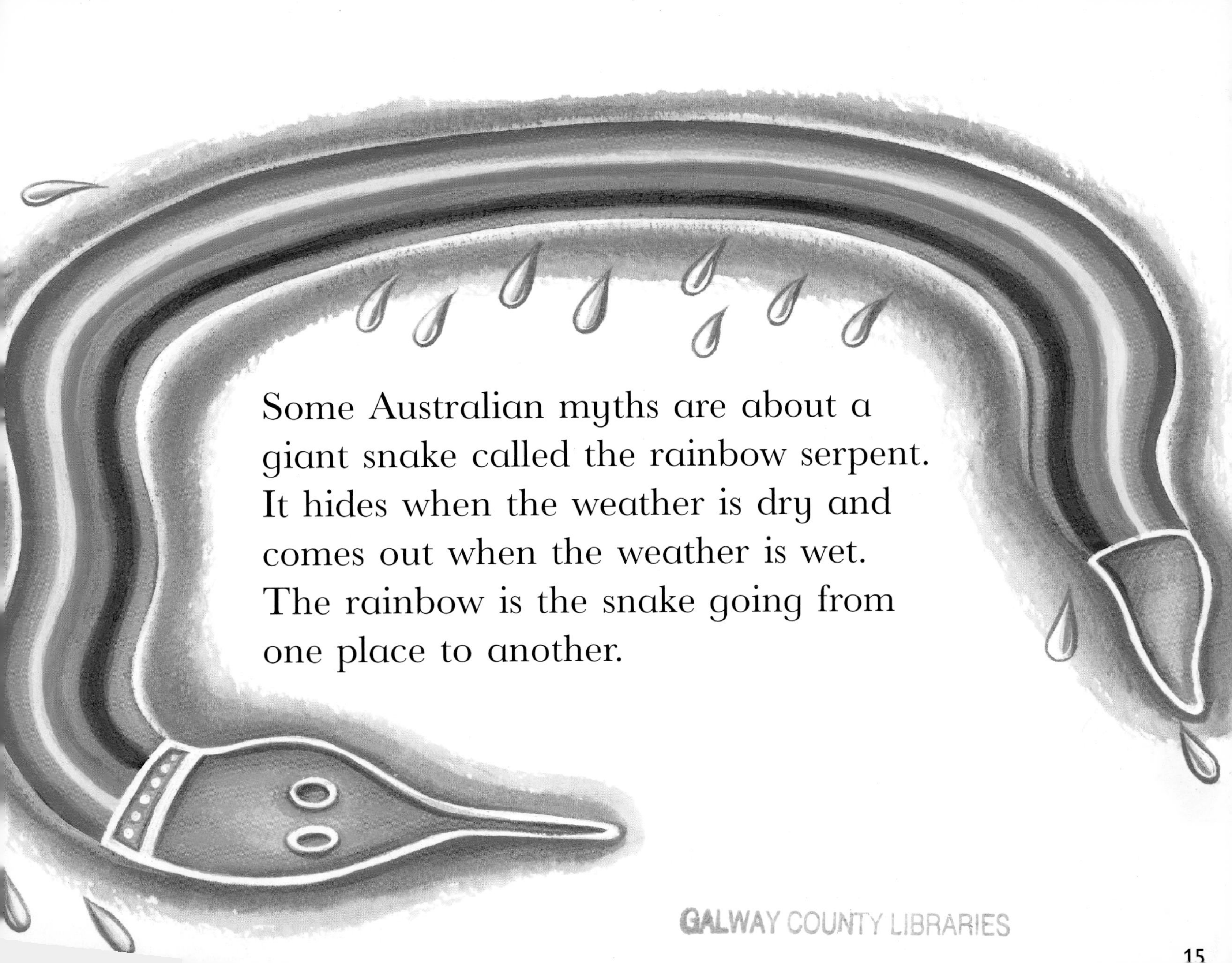

Some Australian myths are about a giant snake called the rainbow serpent. It hides when the weather is dry and comes out when the weather is wet. The rainbow is the snake going from one place to another.

Index

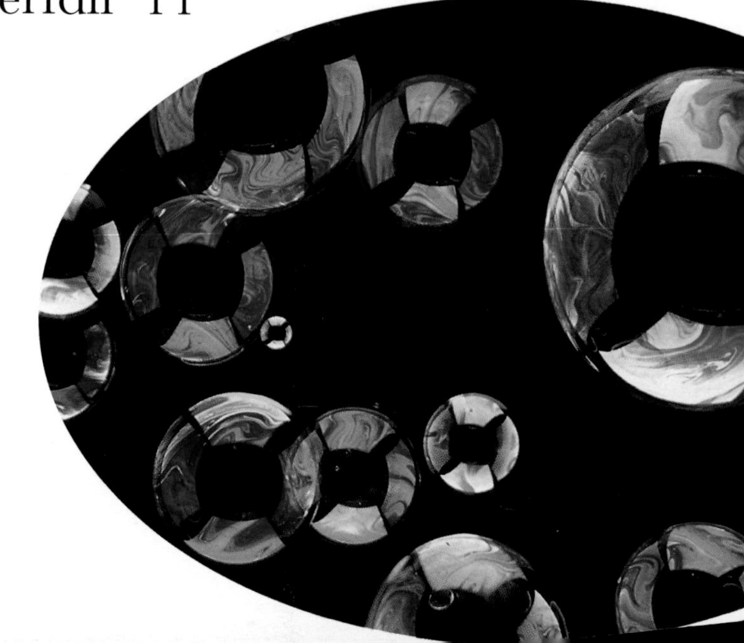